ANIMAL JAM: 2018 A CENTUM BOOK 978-1-911460-60-2
Published in Great Britain by Centum Books Ltd Centum Books, 20 Devon Square,
Newton Abbot, Devon, TQ12 2HR, UK. books@centumbooksltd.co.uk
CENTUM BOOKS Limited Reg. No. 07641486 This edition published 2017. Printed
in China. A CIP catalogue record for this book is available from the British Library.
For more information on Animal Jam's safety and privacy policies, grab a parent
and check out: WWW.ANIMALJAM.COM/RULES and WWW.ANIMALJAM.COM/PRIVACY

2018

This book belongs to the jamtastic

....

Are you ready to PLAY WILD?

TURN TO PAGE 57 TO DISCOVER YOUR FREE CODE TO UNLOCK CONTENT ONLINE AT WWW.ANIMALJAM.COM

centum

PARTY TIME

There's always a party happening in Jamaa. Can you spot 10 differences between these two pictures of the Summer Carnival?

YOU CAN LEARN ALL ABOUT THE LATEST PARTIES BY CLICKING THE PARTY ICON IN THE TOP OF YOUR SCREEN WHEN ONLINE AT WWW.ANIMALJAM.COM

PARTIES LAST FOR THIRTY MINUTES AND THE NEXT ONE STARTS STRAIGHT AFTER, SO YOU NEVER HAVE TO WAIT LONG TO PARTY!

Answers on page 60

JAMAA TOWNSHIP

When you arrive in Jamaa, your first stop should be Jamaa Township.

JAM MART CLOTHING

There is loads to do in the busiest spot in Jamaa. You can shop at Jam Mart Clothing, Jam Mart Furniture and the Diamond Shop. Or have loads of fun at the Sol Arcade and the Pillow Room. Get ready to play wild too as there are lots of fun games in this land including Jamaa Derby and Ducky Dash (although this is a members-only game and you'll need a pet ducky to play). Quack quack!

SOL ARCADE

Head to the Sol Arcade to play all your favourite games from all around Jamaa. From Falling Phantoms to Best Dressed, there is a game for everyone at this fun arcade!

DIAMOND SHOP

Jamaa Township is great for findng accessories for your animal and items to decorate your den.

THERE'S ALWAYS SOMETHING NEW AND EXCITING TO SEE IN JAMMER CENTRAL.

9

APPONDALE

Jamaa's savannah is full of jamtastic animals and its mud pool is the perfect place to relax.

Games fans will love this jammerific land as there are loads of cool games to play, including Fruit Slinger, Pest Control and Disc Toss.

CLAWS 'N PAWS

Find amazing accessories for your pets in Claws 'N Paws, then take some time out in the Appondale Theatre and watch fun videos about all your favourite animals.

CONSERVATION MUSEUM

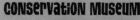

You can donate some Gems to help endangered animals at the Conservation Museum.

CATCH THE GOLDEN DISC
IN DISC TOSS TO
EARN EXTRA GEMS!

ANIMAL MATCH

If you were an animal, what would you be?
Take the quiz to discover your animal match!

Start

Like things fast paced or prefer to take your time?

CHILL OUT ALONE

FAST PACED

take your time

Change your mind a lot or stick to your decisions?

Hang out in a crowd or prefer to chill out alone?

CHILL OUT IN THE COLD

Chill out in the cold or soak up some rays?

HANG OUT IN A CROWD

HOME SWEET HOME

Love to explore or home sweet home?

BIG MEALS

SNACKS

LOVE TO EXPLORE

Love to eat... big meals or lots of snacks?

An early bird and a morning person or more of a night owl?

EARLY BIRD →

You are a cute and friendly sea turtle with a strong mind but lots of poise.

STICK TO YOUR DECISIONS

NIGHT OWL ↓

NGE YOUR MIND

A chatterbox or a better listener?

BETTER LISTENER →

You are an owl and love the night-time, a bit of quiet time and are a keen explorer.

CHATTERBOX ↓

SOAK UP SOME RAYS

Full of energy or need lots of sleep?

FULL OF ENERGY →

You're full of energy just like a bunny and love to hang out with your friends.

NEED YOUR SLEEP ↓

KEEP YOUR COOL

Lose your temper easily or always keep your cool?

LOSE YOUR TEMPER →

You're as tough and hot tempered as a rhino and always ready for lots of fun!

DAWN OF THE ALPHAS

The wonderful world of Jamaa has an exciting and dangerous history. Read on to reveal all!

SQWARK SQWARK!

Jamaa was once home to hundreds of animal species who spent their days playing games, going to parties, building homes and living together as friends.

Mira and Zios, the guardian spirits of Jamaa, gifted each animal species with a Heartstone, a special jewel that contained the essence and secrets of that species.

For many generations, all the Heartstones were kept together beneath the Lost Temple of Zios. Every animal could visit them and see the unique gifts that each species brought to Jamaa.

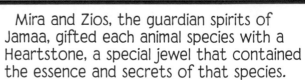

But as time passed, things changed and animals began to fear and mistrust other species. Some animals stopped living together and soon, all the feelings of friendship in Jamaa were gone, and the animals built new villages for their kind only. Koalas lived and talked only with other koalas. So did rhinos and crocodiles.

Before long, all the animals in Jamaa stopped working together to make Jamaa a happy place. Worst of all, many animal species took their Heartstones from the Lost Temple of Zios and hid them in their new villages. It was during this time of division that the dark Phantoms first appeared.

The Phantoms came through dark portals and they quickly spread through the uninhabited regions of Jamaa. Wherever the Phantoms went, they left a trail of destruction. The Phantoms consumed everything in the environment and gave nothing back. They destroyed entire villages the animals had built and left the entire civilization in pieces.

Because animals were spread out in isolated villages, the Phantoms easily conquered these villages one by one. The animals soon discovered that if the Phantoms reached a Heartstone, they could imprison the animals of that species inside it! Each time the Phantoms captured a Heartstone, an entire species disappeared from Jamaa.

BEWARE THE PHANTOMS!

Mira and Zios watched in horror as the Phantoms spread throughout Jamaa. As guardian spirits, it hurt them to see the land they loved become corrupted and they knew they could bring Jamaa back to life if the Phantoms were repelled. In time, they could make the skies and waters clear again and if they could recover the lost Heartstones, thousands of animals could return to Jamaa.

As time drew on, however, the Phantom threat grew only more unstoppable.

Remembering how much the animals had accomplished when they lived and worked together, the remaining six species gathered their Heartstones, left their villages and returned to the Lost Temple of Zios. As the tigers, monkeys, koalas, pandas, bunnies and wolves of Jamaa gathered together for one last stand against the Phantoms, Mira and Zios saw that it would not be enough.

In desperation, the guardian spirits of Jamaa searched for animals who could lead their species. They finally found six extraordinary animals and brought them to Jamaa: Sir Gilbert the regal tiger, Cosmo the knowledgeable koala, Graham the inventive monkey, Greely the mysterious wolf, Liza the curious panda, and Peck the creative bunny.

These were six remarkable animals with different personalities, but they were united in their strength of characters and their respect for the natural world.

SAVE JAMAA!

15

DAWN OF THE ALPHAS

Mira and Zios chose well and these very different animals soon formed a family. To help in battle against the Phantoms, Mira and Zios gave the new leaders Alpha Stones, six special jewels that harnessed the Alphas' abilities and the natural powers of Jamaa. With these stones, the six chosen animals became Alphas, the heroes chosen to save Jamaa in its darkest hour!

The Alphas set about making a plan that utilized each of their unique abilities to defeat the Phantoms. Once the plan was finalised, they joined the rest of the animals who had gathered together to face the flood of Phantoms before them. When the animals saw the magnificent Alphas, they felt their own bravery return. The Alphas felt strength flowing through them and with many roars, howls, and cheers they all stormed into battle.

The battle for Jamaa was epic, with the animals and Alphas fighting not just for themselves, but also for the beautiful land that Jamaa once was. Animals that were once scared of the Phantoms found new courage, and animals that had shunned and despised others worked side by side with different species.

As the animals marched forward, the Phantoms escaped by fleeing into their dark portals. But just as the last of the Phantoms were retreating, they overtook Zios and vanished with him into a portal. Mira quickly dove into a dark portal, following Zios and the Phantoms, disappearing as the portal closed.

The sudden absence of Zios and Mira was a tragic blow to the animals, yet despite their sadness, they realized that for the first time many of them could remember, Jamaa was free of the Phantoms!

Jamaa had been saved, but the damage the Phantoms had caused was everywhere. Plants and trees were sick, clouds of poison smoke hung in the air, and the land itself was littered with burnt rubbish that seemed to follow the Phantoms wherever they went.

The Alphas knew it would be the responsibility of every animal in Jamaa, including themselves, to return the land to its former glory.

While the animals worked hard to rebuild, cleansing power from the Alpha Stones flowed through the Alphas and into the land. Soon, the rivers were running clear, the trees regained their leaves, and the air was fresh and crisp. The pristine beauty of Jamaa had spread from the top of Mt. Shiveer to the bottom of Deep Blue.

ALPHAS RULE!

During this time, Peck stayed in Jamaa Township to protect the village and help new animals that came to Jamaa, while the other Alphas separated to explore lost lands and track the Phantoms to their source. They were able to restore many of the lands that had been taken over by the Phantoms, and many Heartstones were returned. Animals trapped inside the Heartstones were freed to return to their homes, and they were welcomed by all their animal friends. In a short time, the world of Jamaa began to resemble the beautiful world it once was!

TIME TO PLAY WILD!

HOORAY!

Crystal Sands

If you love the water, sand and surf, splash down in this aqua-amazing land.

you are here

CAPTAIN MELVILLE'S JUICE HUT

Waterslides, waterfalls and seaside fun are just some of the things you can enjoy in Crystal Sands.

Be sure to check out all these amazing games in Crystal Sands: Overflow, Double Up, The Claw and the Pet Wash.

TIERNEY'S AQUARIUM

Dr Tierney Thys has travelled the world to study ocean life and shares all the wonders she has discovered in Tierney's Aquarium. If you love gadgets you'll love all the cool tools on her tech bench like underwater cameras and shark suits. If you've got a question about ocean life, head to the theatre to ask Tierney a question.

Jump into Jamaa's oceans from either of the docks and start exploring the water!

18

AMERICAN CROCODILES
CAN LIVE UP TO AROUND
70 YEARS IN THE WILD.

WORD WIZARD

Can you fit all the animal names below into the grid opposite?

- ☐ BUNNY
- ☐ CHEETAH
- ☐ EAGLE
- ☐ ELEPHANT
- ☐ FOX
- ☐ GIRAFFE
- ☐ HORSE
- ☐ LLAMA
- ☐ LION

- ☐ KANGAROO
- ☐ KOALA
- ☐ MONKEY
- ☐ PENGUIN
- ☐ RACCOON
- ☐ SEAL
- ☐ SHARK
- ☐ TIGER
- ☐ WOLF

Answers on page 60

21

CORAL CANYONS

With its beautiful red sandstone cliffs this rocky land is a great place to explore if you're up for a desert adventure.

WILD EXPLORERS TENT

It may be a desert, but there is plenty to do in this land, with loads of colouring and painting activities, science experiments and animal facts to enjoy.

DEN SHOP

You can play Best Dressed, Long Shot and Sky High, and also shop for all kinds of treasures at Royal Ridge and the Den Shop.

ROYAL RIDGE

SALE

Step out of the heat and into the mysterious Epic Wonders, a magical shop hidden in a cave under the waterfall.

HYNEAS PATROL AND
MARK THEIR TERRITORY BY
DEPOSITING A STRONG SMELL
FROM THEIR BOTTOMS
ON STALKS OF GRASS.

ANiMAL Spotter

The pictures on the opposite page may all look the same as the one below, but something is different in each one. Can you spot what?

1

2

3

4

5

6

Answers on page 60

PICK A PENGUIN

Can you spot the odd penguin out in each row below?

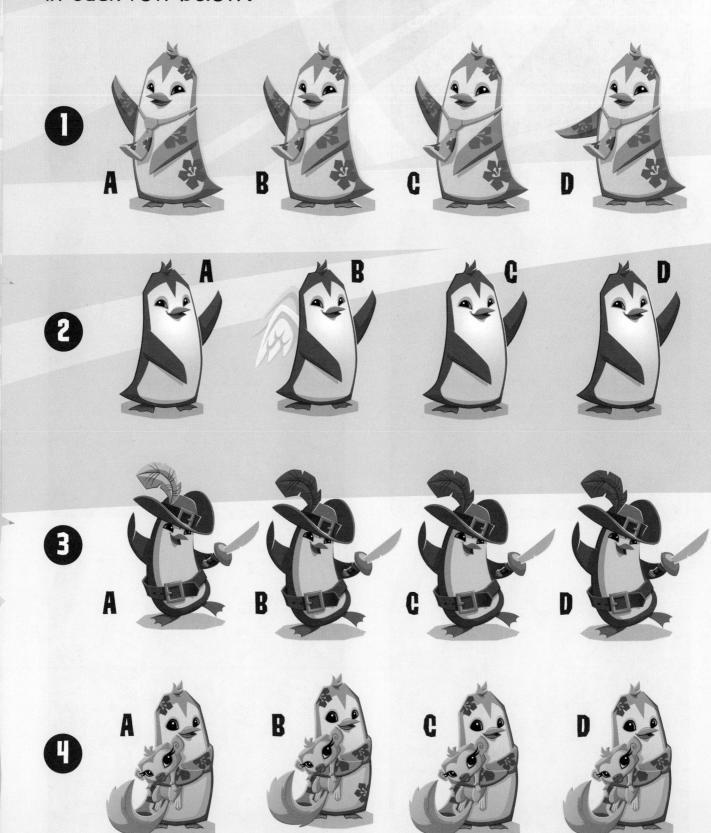

1 A B C D

2 A B C D

3 A B C D

4 A B C D

SOME PENGUINS LIVE IN COLD areas LIKE ANTARCTICA BUT OTHERS are FOUND IN WARMER CLIMATES LIKE THE GALAPAGOS ISLANDS!

5 A B C D

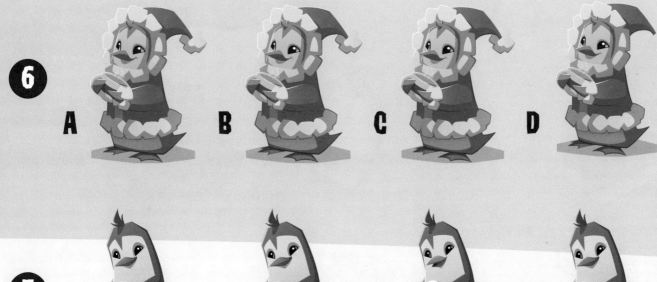

6 A B C D

7 A B C D

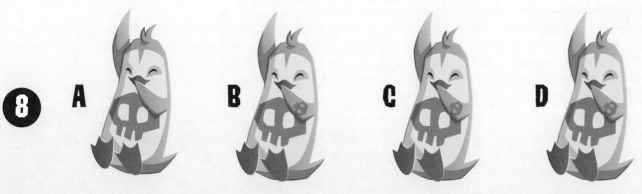

8 A B C D

Answers on page 60

KIMBARA OUTBACK

Take a trip down under and check out all the wild and wonderful things to see and do in this sandy hot spot!

you are here

Kimbara Outback is a great destination if you're looking for accessories or den items. Head to Outback Imports for items that are built to last the harsh conditions of the desert.

KOALAS ONLY LIVE IN AUSTRALIA AND CAN SLEEP UP TO 18 HOURS A DAY.

Visit the amazing Gabby's Animal Hospital to watch awesome videos and learn from Gabby Wild about what it takes to help wild animals and be a wildlife conservationist and veterinarian.

GABBY'S ANIMAL HOSPITAL

Did you know that the letters on the eye chart in Gabby's Animal Hospital spell out the names of the Alphas?

29

SHADOW SPOT

Can you match the animal to its shadow as they enjoy the flames of the campfire?

Answers on page 61

sky soarers

Which eagle's route through the clouds will get them to the ground in the least time?

start 1

start 2

END

Look up when you're in Jamaa, as there are always lots of amazing animals flying around.

Answers on page 61

31

seek and find

Can you find all the jammerific animals below in the wordsearch opposite?

BUNNY	GIRAFFE
CROCODILE	KANGAROO
DEER	HYENA
DOLPHIN	MONKEY
EAGLE	TIGER
ELEPHANT	RACCOON
FOX	RHINO

```
E B B I G Q Q X R E G V S W N
A C X U L G O L L V V X B O N
G R J N N F S E H J Y N O X N
L O W V V N P K J F R C K C Y
E C R S J H Y X U R C Y H R I
J O O X A C I P R A R E G I T
S D Z N O H S O R G E G V E Q
P I T E I Y O K W P I H A E A
D L S F L H E A N C J S U A E
T E P F G S R P Z I N Y C B R
U W C A X D P D I I H P O H E
W G I R V W F C X Y M P Y B E
A V H I P M O N K E Y E L W D
E X Y G Q O O R A G N A K O W
C W S J R X H O N A Q P M O D
```

Answers on page 61

PET DOODLE

Turn these squiggles into lots of pawsome pets!

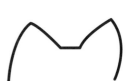

How many did you squeeze onto the page?

Mt. Shiveer

No visitor to Jamaa should miss its impressive highest mountain, or sliding all the way down it! Wheeee-eee!

Once you've tried out the ice slide show off your ice-skating skills on the ice patch.

Mt. Shiveer may be cold but there are plenty of places to warm up. Slurp on a delicious hot choccie, buy some warm and cosy clothes or soak up some heat in the hot springs.

Hot Cocoa Hut

Hot Cocoa Hut

It's rumoured the ice patch is unbreakable, but that doesn't stop visitors to Mt. Shiveer jumping up and down to try and crack it.

SNOW LEOPARDS LIVE
IN HIGH ALTITUDES
IN ASIA AND LIKE
TO BE ALONE.

PAWSOME PATTERNS

Make these animals totally unique with some cool colours and patterns!

sarepia Forest

If you're looking to play wild, explore the exciting woods of Sarepia Forest.

Treetop Gardens

Flag Shop

Plant lovers can spend their Gems in the wild woods with lots of great shops to visit including the Flag Shop, Treetop Gardens, Topiary Shop and Theater Shop.

There are loads of jamtastic games too, so don't miss Wind Rider, Super Sort, Hedge Hog, Pill Bugs, Popcorn Machine, The Claw, Swoopy Eagle and Disc Toss.

All animals love sliding through the woods on the whizzy slide and warming up (or having a boogie) by the campfire.

sarepia Theatre

VIDEOS

Sarepia Theatre is the perfect place to grab some popcorn to munch while checking out some videos about all the weird and wonderful animals in the world.

There are forests all over the world and environments like forests can be found in the world's oceans too.

WILD WOLVES ARE LIKE DOGS AND THEY LOVE TO PLAY AND HOWL TOGETHER!

BiG aND SMaLL

There are all kinds of amazing animals in the world. Read on to discover some fun facts about the BIGGEST and smallest!

The largest spiders in the world are **goliath bird-eating tarantulas**. Yes, as the name suggests, these spiders are large enough to eat birds!

Blue whales are the world's biggest animals and are about 30m long. Their tongues alone can weigh as much as an elephant and their hearts as much as a car. **African elephants** are the world's largest land animals and can grow to around 7.5 m long and 3.3 m tall.

Etruscan shrews are a small species of shrew and grow to around 5 cm in length. That's small enough to fit on a spoon. To keep their tiny bodies warm they have to eat often and, while they may look cute, they kill their prey with their venomous bite. Bumblebee bats (also known as Kitti's hog-nose bats) are another tiny mammal and only weigh about 2 g.

Giraffes are the tallest animals in the world and male giraffes can reach up to 5.5 m tall. Baby giraffes are around 1.8 m tall when they are born. They also have the longest tail of any land animal.

The smallest birds are the bee hummingbirds (*Mellisuga helenae*) of Cuba and the Isle of Youth. Males measure 57 mm in length, half of which is taken up by the bill and tail, and weigh 1.6 g. Females are slightly larger.

Tarantula hawk wasps have one of the most painful stings of any insects on the planet. They eat tarantulas and are the largest wasps in the world. Bullet ants are the largest ant species in the world and have a toxic sting that can paralyse animals the size of a human.

LOtS tO SPOt

Put a tick below the animals that you can spot enjoying themselves in Jamaa Township.

Answers on page 61

LOST TEMPLE OF ZIOS

Head deep into this mysterious jungle for plenty of excitement and adventure.

Whether you're looking for den artifacts or Alpha statues, the Mystery Emporium in the Chamber of Knowledge has you covered.

There are also loads of jammerific games to play, from Falling Phantoms and Temple of Trivia to Mira Says and Gem Ball!

BRADY'S LAB

Dr Brady Barr is a herpetologist, which is a scientist who studies amphibians and reptiles. At his lab and theatre you can learn about some wild science experiments and watch awesome videos of amazing close enounters with all kinds of weird and wonderful wildlife!

MYSTERY EMPORIUM

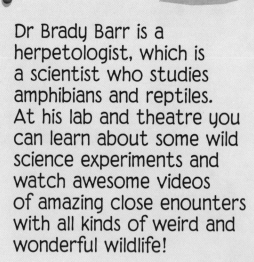

What's your favourite thing in this exciting land?

THE RAINFORESTS ON OUR PLANET ARE HOME TO AROUND HALF THE WORLD'S ANIMAL AND PLANT SPECIES.

Make a Thaumatrope

Follow the simple steps below to create an owlstanding optical illusion turning two pictures into one image.

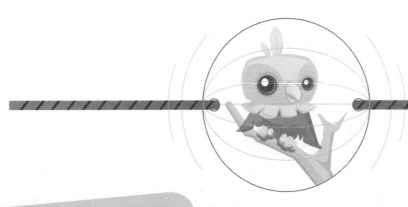

What you need:

- templates on page 63
- scissors
- hole punch
- string
- glue
- card

What you do:

1. Cut out the thaumatrope templates opposite and stick them onto some card.
2. Glue the corresponding templates together, with the images facing out.
3. Punch a hole on the left and right side of the template.
4. Tie a piece of string through each hole. Your thaumatrope should look like the finished example on this page.
5. Twist the string and let the thaumatrope spin! The two pictures should look like they are creating one single image!
6. Now try and come up with your own cool thaumatrope design!

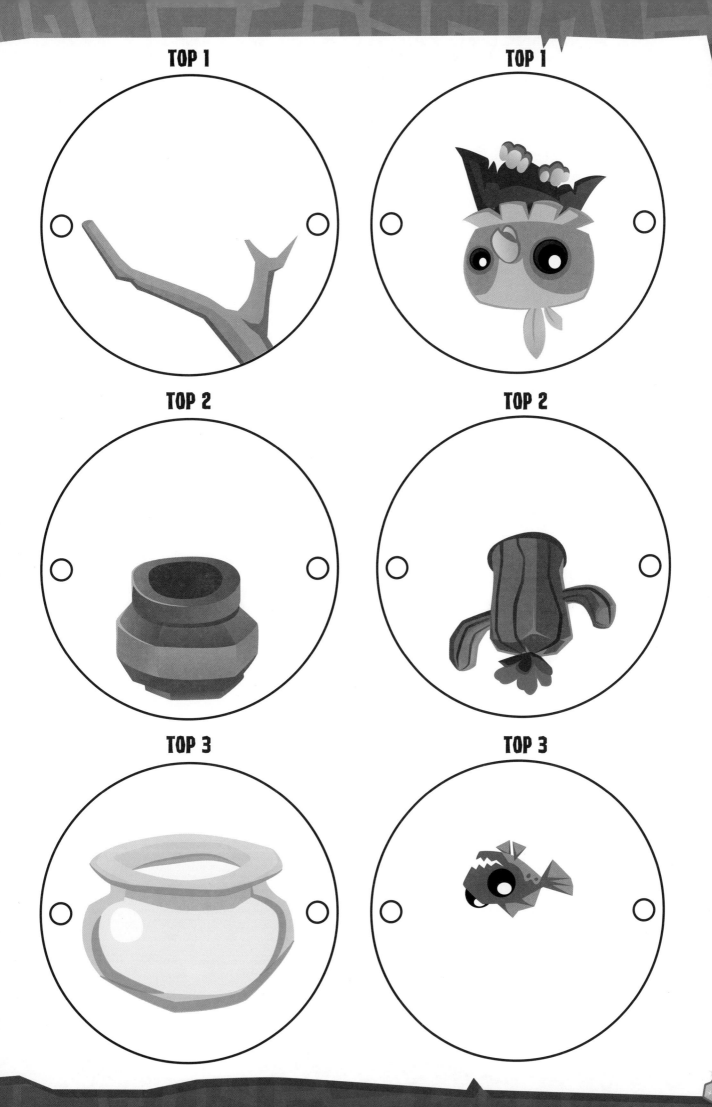

TOP 1

TOP 1

TOP 2

TOP 2

TOP 3

TOP 3

49

TOP 1

TOP 1

TOP 2

TOP 2

TOP 3

TOP 3

TOP 1

TOP 1

PHANTOMS BEWARE

Grab your boldest black pen and colour in all these pesky Phantoms.

UNDER THE SEA

Dive in for some splash-tastic fun in Jamaa's oceans, reefs and deep blue seas.

DEEP BLUE

Deep Blue is the deepest part of the ocean in Jamaa. Play Phantoms' Treasure and find all the hidden objects and watch out for the almost alien-like sea creatures that live here.

CRYSTAL REEF

This rainbow-bright underworld is bursting with plant and animal life. Spot marine animals including clownfish and marlin and shop at Flippers 'N Fins for your marine pets. And climb your way up the food chain by playing a game of Eat 'Em Up.

YOU ARE HERE

Bahari Bay

All of Jamaa's ocean animals should stop by and see everything Bahari Bay has to offer. In this beautiful bay you can shop at Bahari Bargains, the only shop which which sells ocean accessories. Show off your fashion sense by playing a few rounds of Best Dressed - Oceans and race to the finish line in Splash and Dash.

Kani Cove

Go exploring and swim around the amazing shipwreck in Kani Cove - watch out for any pirates along the way! Don't forget to shop at Sunken Treasures for cool items for your ocean den.

THE MARIANA TRENCH IS THE DEEPEST SPOT ON OUR PLANET. IT'S IN THE PACIFIC OCEAN AND OVER 10 KM DEEP.

MEMORY MUDDLE

Take a good look at the picture below and try to remember as much as you can, then cover the page and answer the questions opposite.

1 What shape glasses is the horse wearing?

A moon shape
B banana shape
C star shape

2 How many mushrooms are there?

A one
B four
C none

3 What is the white bunny holding?

A a carrot
B a hat
C an ice cream

4 What colour wings is the giraffe wearing?

A blue
B orange
C pink

5 Which of these owl shadows is not in the picture?

A   B   C

Answers on page 61

55

ANiMAL ANTiCS

Looking for some jamtastic games to play on the weekend or after school? Read on!

ANiMAL ALPHABET

- Gather together a group of players and take turns to shout out the name of an animal.
- The first player must name an animal starting with the letter A, the second player with the letter B and so on through all the letters of the alphabet.
- If a player can't think of an animal they're out.
- The last player left in wins!

ANiMAL HiDE AND SEEK

- Gather together a group of players and take it in turns for one player to be the seeker and the others to hide.
- If the seeker gets close to where each player is hiding, the hiding player must make the noise of an animal. (For example they must bark like a dog or roar like a lion.)
- If the seeker guesses which player is hiding, that player is out and they must join the seeker to look for the other players.
- If the seeker can't guess which player is hiding, they have to close thier eyes, count to 30 and let the player hide again.
- The last player to be found wins!
- The first player to be found is the next seeker.

CRACK THE CODE

Circle every third letter or number in the panel below to reveal a secret code to unlock content online at WWW.ANIMALJAM.COM

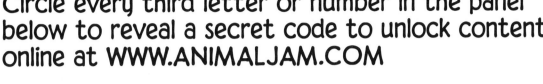

T D (A) B 2 N G L N

T 3 U K M A Q X

L Y B 2 T P P 6

M L O R A 2 Z Y

A

THIS CODE WILL REWARD YOU WITH FREE GEMS!

Enter your code on the homescreen WWW.ANIMALJAM.COM

COOL COLOURS

Colour all these jamtastic animals in your favourite colours.

ANSWERS

P6-7

P21

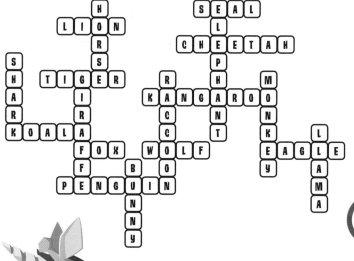

P25

1

2

3

4

5

6

P26-27

1-D   2-B   3-A   4-B

5-B   6-D   7-C   8-A

P30

D	C	D	B	A	E

P31

Start 1 is the quickest

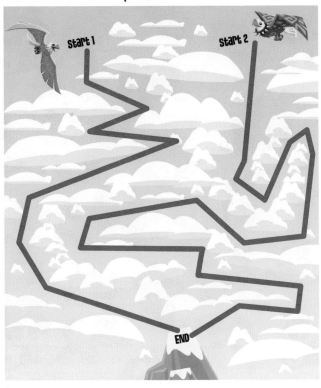

P32-33

```
E B B I G Q Q X R E G V S W N
A C X U L G O L L V V X B O N
G R J N N F S E H J Y N O X N
L O W V V N P K J F R C K C Y
E C R S J H Y X U R C Y H R I
J O O X A C I P R A R E G I T
S D Z N O H S O R G E G V E Q
P I T E I Y O K W P I H A E A
D L S F L H E A N C J S U A E
T E P F G S R P Z I N Y C B R
U W C A X D P D I I H P O H E
W G I R V W F C X Y M P Y B E
A V H I P M O N K E Y E L W D
E X Y G Q O O R A G N A K O W
C W S J R X H O N A Q P M O D
```

P44-45

P55

1-C, 2-B, 3-B, 4-C, 5-C